Contents

Come Out, Chip!

Bird is out.

Chip is not out.

Chip is in.

Bird said, "Come out, Chip.
You and I can run."

Chip said, "I will not run."

Bird said, "Will you come out?"

Chip said, "Yes, Bird.
I will come out.
I will not run."

Get Up, Bear!

Bird said, "Bear is not out."

Chip said, "Is Bear in?"

Bird said, "Bear is in.
Bear is not up."

Chip said, "I can get Bear up."

Chip said, "Get up, Bear!"

Bear said, "No, no, no!
I will not get up."

Chip said, "You will get up, Bear."

Bird said, "Bear is up!"

Chip said, "Go out, Bear.
You will go out!"

The Boat

Chip said, "We can go out.
We can go out in the boat."

Bird said, "Will you go out, Bear?"

Bear said, "Yes, I will go out
in the boat."

Bird said, "Can this boat go?"

Chip said, "Yes, it can.
We can get this boat to go."

Bear said, "We can do this.
We can get the big boat to go."

Bird said, "Can we do it?"

Bear said, "Chip and I will do it.
We will get the big boat to go."

Chip said, "The boat will not go."

"We can not go out in this big boat," said Bird.

Bear said, "Yes, we can. I can get this boat to go."

"This will do it," said Bear.

"Yes," said Chip.
"The boat will go!"

"We can go out in the boat,"
said Bird.

The Balloon

"Get up, Bear!" said Bird.

Bear said, "What is it?"

Chip said, "It is a big balloon."

18

Bear said, "What can we do
in a balloon?"

Bird said, "We can go up in it.
It is fun to go up in a balloon."

Chip said, "You and Bear go.
I will not go up in a balloon."

"Can we go up in the balloon,
Dog?" said Bear.

Dog said, "Yes.
You can go up in this balloon.
You can go up now."

"I will not go up," said Chip.

"It will be fun to go up,"
said Bear.

Bird said, "Yes, Chip.
It will be fun."

Bear said, "Get in, Chip!"

"This is fun!" said Chip.
"It is fun to be up in a balloon."

"It is not fun," said Bear.
"Can we go down now?"

Dog said, "We can go down.
We can go down now."

Chip said, "It is fun to go up in a balloon."

"You and Bird can go in the balloon.

I will go in the boat," said Bear.

The Plane

"How do you do, Turtle,"
said Bear.

"How do you do, Bear,"
said Turtle.

Bear said, "What is that?
What will that be?"

"This will be a plane,"
said Turtle.

"Can we make a plane?"
said Chip.

Turtle said, "Yes.
You can make a plane."

"It will be fun to make
a plane," said Bird.

"How can we make a plane?"
said Bear.

"This is what you can do,"
said Turtle.

"That will make a big plane,"
said Bird.

"What is that?" said Chip.

"This will make the plane go,"
said Bird.

"Will it fit?" said Bear.

"I can make it fit," said Bird.
"This is how I will do it."

"You did it!" said Turtle.
"Now you can go out
with the plane."

Bear, Chip, and Bird will go
out with the plane.

"We did it," said Bird.

"Yes, we did make this plane," said Chip.

"Now I can make the plane go," said Bear.

"I will run with the plane."

29

Fun with Bear

Bear can not go out.
Bear can not run.
Chip and Bird will help Bear.

"How can we help Bear?"
said Bird.

"What can we do?"

"We can go to see Bear,"
said Chip.

"We can take this to Bear."

"I will take this," said Bird.
"Bear will have fun with this."

"Yes, it will be fun," said Chip.
"Now come and help.
I can not get the things to fit."

"I will make things fit," said Bird.
"Can we go to see Bear now?"

"No, we have to get flowers,"
said Chip.

"We will take flowers to Bear."

Chip said, "How do you do, Bear.
We have come to see you."

Bird said, "What can I do
with the flowers?"

"The flowers can go in that,"
said Bear.

"What fun this is," said Bear.

"I can not go out.

I can not run.

I can have fun with you,"
said Bear.

"Yes, and we can have fun
with you," said Chip.

Can Bear Do It?

Bear sees that the things
will not fit.

Bear takes the things out.

What will Bear do?

"Chip, will you help me?"
said Bear.

"Will you take some things?"

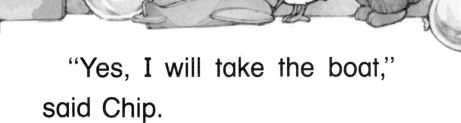

"Yes, I will take the boat,"
said Chip.

"I will take the balloons, too."

"I will take the plane," said Bird.

"That will be a big help,"
said Bear.

"Turtle, will you help me?
Will you take some things from me?" said Bear.

"Yes, I will take this from you," said Turtle.

"I will take some things, too," said Dog.

38

"Come in, Pig," said Bear.
"See what I have in here.
Will you take some things
from me?"

"I will see what you have.
You can see what I have, too,"
said Pig.

"Pig, you have good things here," said Bear.

"I will take this big flower.

I will take this big dog, too.

I will take this,

and this,

and this."

40

"Bear, this is not good.
You can not make things
fit in here," said Bird.

"Yes, I can," said Bear.

Stop and Go!

"Come and play, Bear," said Chip.
"Come and play with us."

"I want to play with you,"
said Bear.
"I can not get out to you."

"Yes, you can," said Bird.
"I will help you."

"Look, Bear," said Bird.
"Look at how I do it."

"Now you can play with us.
Do you want to play Stop and
Go?" said Chip.

"Yes," said Bear.
"I want to play Stop and Go."

"I can not do this," said Bear.
"I will fall."

"You will not fall," said Bird.
"Look at us.
Do what we do."

Bear falls down and gets up.
Bear gets up and falls down.

Bear said, "Chip! Bird!
I have to stop.
I can not do this.
I have to get some things."

48

"Look at me," said Bear.
"Now I can play Stop and Go.
Now I can have fun, too."

50

A New Friend

by Marjorie Allen Anderson

They've taken in the furniture:
I watched them carefully.
I wondered, "Will there be a child
Just right to play with me?"

So I peeked through the garden fence
(I couldn't wait to see).
I found the little boy next door
Was peeking back at me.

Come to See Me

*by Florence Parry Heide
and Roxanne Heide Pierce*

"I want to see you,"
said Grandpa.
"I want you to come here."

"I want to see you, too,"
said Skip.
"I want to have fun with you."

"I want to see you, too, Grandpa," said Jill.

"I want to be with you and have fun.

How can we come to see you?"

"I can help you get here,"
said Grandpa.

"I can help you come to see me."

"Can you get some balloons for us?" said Skip.

"The balloons will take us up and up.

The balloons can take us to see you."

"No, I can not do that," said Grandpa.

"You can not get here with balloons.

You will fall with balloons."

"Can you get a big bird?"
said Jill.

"A big bird can help us
come to see you."

"No bird is that big,"
said Grandpa.

"A bird can not get you here."

"Can a plane take us to you?"
said Jill.

"A plane can take us,"
said Skip.
"A plane can take us to you."

"Yes, you can come in a plane,"
said Grandpa.
"I will see you and be with you.
We will have fun."

Word Helper

"Word Helper" develops readiness for dictionary skills and provides students with a reference for words they may wish to use in their writing. Example sentences for all new words in this book are provided. Illustrated sentences are followed by ■.

Aa

a   This is **a** big dog.

at   Look **at** the flowers. ■

Bb

balloon   This is a big **balloon.** ■

balloons   Did Bird get some **balloons?**

be   I will **be** in the boat.

big   The **big** dog can run.

boat   The **boat** will not go.

58

Dd

did I **did** not go up in the balloon.

do I **do** not run.

down I will come **down.** ∎

Ff

fall Did Bear **fall** down?

falls Bear **falls** down now.

fit It will not **fit** in the boat.

flower Look at the **flower.**

flowers I can see the **flowers.** ∎

for Turtle will make a plane **for** us.

59

from   We will run **from** the dog.

fun   It is **fun** to run. ■

Gg

get   I will **get** the dog. ■

gets   Chip **gets** some things.

good   I will make a **good** plane.

Hh

have   We **have** fun in a boat.

help   I will **help** you.

here   The pig is in **here.** ■

how   This is **how** we do it.

Ll

look

Come **look** at the flowers. ■

Mm

make

I can **make** a plane. ■

me

You can run with **me.**

Nn

now

I can go up **now.** ■

Pp

plane

A **plane** can go up. ■

play

I will **play** with the balloon.

Ss

said   Bird **said,** "I will go out."

see   I **see** the bird. ■

sees   Bird **sees** me.

some   We will get **some** flowers.

stop   We will **stop** the boat now.

Tt

take   We can **take** the boat out.

takes   Bear **takes** some things.

that   Can we go in **that** balloon?

things   Get some **things** for Bird, too.

this   I will go in **this** boat.

to   I can run **to** the boat.

too   Turtle is here.
Pig is here, **too.** ■

Uu

up   Bird said, "Get **up!**" ■

us   The dog ran with **us.**

Ww

want   We **want** to have fun.

we   **We** can go to the boat.

what   **What** is that thing?

with   Bear is **with** Chip. ■

Word List

The following words are introduced in this book. Each is listed beside the number of the page on which it first appears.

Come Out, Chip!
(4–7)

6 said

Get Up, Bear!
(8–11)

8 get
up

The Boat
(12–17)

12 boat
we
13 this
to
14 do - *dew*
big

The Balloon
(18–23)

18 balloon
what
a
19 fun
20 now
21 be

22 down

The Plane
(24–29)

24 plane
how
that
25 make
27 fit
28 did
with

Fun with Bear
(30–35)

30 help
31 see
take
32 have
things
33 flowers

Can Bear Do It?
(36–41)
36 sees
takes
37 me

some
balloons
too
38 from
39 here
40 good
flower

Stop and Go!
(42–49)

42 stop
43 play
us
want
44 look
at
45 fall
46 falls
gets

Come to See Me
(52–57)

55 for

3
4
5
J 6

64